Sarah's Seed

CHAPTER 1
CORONADO HILLS ELEMENTARY

Sarah found a seed.

"I will grow a beanstalk,"
she said.

"No you won't,"
said Carla.

"I will watch it grow higher than a house," said Sarah.

"No you won't," said Carla.

"I will watch it grow right up into the sky," said Sarah.

"No you won't," said Carla.

"I will watch it grow right through the clouds," said Sarah.

"No you won't," said Carla.

"I will climb right up
to the top,"
said Sarah.

"No you won't,"
said Carla.

"I might even get
to the moon,"
said Sarah.

"No you won't,"
said Carla.

"Why not?" asked Sarah.

Carla laughed.
"Because it's a
pumpkin seed!" she said.